Man Takes a Drink

At the punch-bowl's brink
Let the thirsty think
   What they say in Japan:
"First the man takes a drink,
Then the drink takes a drink,
   Then the drink takes the man!"

—An Adage from the Orient

Man Takes a Drink

FACTS AND PRINCIPLES
ABOUT ALCOHOL

BY

JOHN C. FORD S.J.

Professor of Moral and Pastoral Theology
Weston College, Weston, Mass.

P. J. KENEDY & SONS
New York

CUM PERMISSU SUPERIORUM

NIHIL OBSTAT: RT. REV. EDWARD G. MURRAY, LL.D.
                                                    Censor Librorum
IMPRIMATUR: ✠ RICHARD J. CUSHING, DD., LL.D.
                                                    Archbishop of Boston
Boston
December 9, 1954

LIBRARY OF CONGRESS CATALOG CARD NUMBER: 55-6439

Copyright, 1955, P. J. Kenedy & Sons, New York ©

PRINTED IN THE UNITED STATES OF AMERICA

Foreword

FATHER FORD has performed a great service in writing this book. It is desperately needed, for it tackles fairly, objectively, and with forthright clarity, one of the most baffling and complex problems of modern life: the use of beverage alcohol.

We moderns have been ill-prepared to meet the problems surrounding the use of alcohol, whether they be problems of decision, of excessive drinking, or the tragic problem of alcoholism. We have not been taught adequately, largely because unbiased, factual information has not been easily available. Although much has been written on this subject, unfortunately a large part of it has been biased propaganda, designed to win converts for one side or the other in the age-old struggle between "wets" and "drys."

Father Ford does not approach the problem from either platform. A leading moral theologian of the Roman Catholic Church, his approach is naturally a Catholic one. He speaks often of temperance, or moderation, as a virtue. He practices this virtue in his writing, for the book is both mod-

erate and temperate in tone, a natural outgrowth of the fact that it is solidly based on sound scientific findings. Father Ford knows his subject. He has not allowed his eminence as a teacher to prevent his continued study in this field. His broad knowledge and his lucid, direct presentation should appeal to many points of view, since his Catholic background has imposed no limitations. People of all faiths will find it clearly informative and helpful. Catholics in particular may well use it as a full and complete textbook for their own approach to drinking.

There is no doubt that a better approach to drinking is one of the greatest needs of our time. We, as a nation, have been careless about it. We have not had sufficient respect for the power of alcohol, or sufficient knowledge of its good or bad effects. We are not alone in this, for the problems connected with alcohol are world-wide, and alcoholism is, likewise, a world-wide problem.

Father Ford has given due consideration to alcoholism in these pages. He recognizes its vast importance, and he is fully aware of the mountain of ignorance and misconception that must be moved before we can hope to bring this scourge of mankind under control. Chapter five probably could be called the keystone of the arch he is building: an arch named "The Sane Approach," through

which many people may be able to walk to sobriety, health, and happiness.

It is my firm conviction that all people of all ages must be put in possession of the facts in this matter. It is far too important in the lives of us all to avoid or evade any longer. Sooner or later, decisions will have to be made by millions of people, young and old. Father Ford's clear exposition will enable many of them to make their decisions in the light of knowledge. In fact, it will bring many, who perhaps had not realized the need before, to the point of decision.

For these reasons, I hope for the widest possible reading of this book. I am sure I bespeak the gratitude of all of us working in this field to Father Ford for his great contributions. *Depth Psychology, Morality and Alcoholism* already has had widespread effectiveness in increasing the understanding of alcoholism. *Man Takes A Drink* should carry that understanding even further, and bring it to many people, particularly young people, who might otherwise be headed for years of heartbreak and tragedy.

This book is a tool of prevention. Let us hope that it is a tool that will be used widely and well.

MARTY MANN, *Executive Director*
The National Committee on Alcoholism

Table of Contents

Man Takes a Drink

CHAPTER 1

Making Personal Decisions

————— • • —————

TOO MANY PEOPLE who have decisions to make never really make them. They drift or they follow the crowd. One of the reasons is that they are confused. They are not in possession of sufficient facts and principles to make a sensible decision.

This book is not written to convince you that you should be a teetotaler. Nor is it written to convince you that moderate drinking is the thing to do. It is written to help you *decide for yourself,* on the basis of scientific facts and spiritual principles, whether to drink or not, whether to stop drinking, or whether your way of drinking is truly moderate, that is, befitting a human being.

It sets forth some scientific facts about alcohol. It explains what is meant by the virtue of sobriety. It explains that there are two ways of practicing this virtue, either by abstaining from drinking, or by keeping one's drinking within the bounds of

moderation. It answers questions about excessive drinking, for instance, is it wrong, and if so, how wrong is it to get high or tight or drunk. Finally, it describes a special kind of drinking, the addiction to drink called alcoholism.

SCOPE OF THE PROBLEM

In some countries, it would seem very strange to the majority of the population to give special thought and reflection to the question of drinking or not drinking. In some countries the serious abuse of drink is relatively infrequent, and its moderate use is so much a part of the national habit that alcohol problems are relatively infrequent, too.

Unfortunately this is not true in the United States (and many other countries). We have serious and widespread problems which go hand-in-hand with the excessive use of alcohol. For example, we have about 4,000,000 alcoholics who create devastating problems for themselves and for the many more millions who live or work with them. An alcoholic is a person who keeps drinking excessively, even though his drinking causes serious problems in his life. He is generally unable to stop drinking for good, even if he wants to, without outside help.

We have millions of other drinkers who would not be classed as alcoholics, but whose frequent excess causes problems in the family, on the job, on the highway; problems of health, criminal problems, and moral problems.

However, the alcohol picture is not all black. There are millions of people who make use of alcoholic beverages with considerable regularity and yet rarely pass the bounds of moderation.

It is because the picture is many-sided that people are confused. The evils of drink are decried by preachers and prohibitionists. Yet, artful advertising constantly plays up the advantages and prestige of social drinking to a public educated to respond to commercial color and repetition.

A drunkard on the street is treated as a joke, but he is put in jail for his offense. Drunkenness is the point of endless witticisms, but we have been taught that drunkenness is a sin that offends God. Parents warn their children of the dangers of drink, but they do not practice what they preach.

The general confusion is made worse by the misinformation and legends circulated about drinking. It's good for a cold. It's bad for your health. Drinking capacity is a sign of manliness. Alcohol is a stimulant. As they stand here, all these statements are false.

POINTS OF DECISION

A large number of people in this country, young and old, are faced with certain decisions about alcohol.

1. To drink or not to drink.
2. If you decide to drink, you must decide what is moderate drinking for you.
3. If you have trouble with drink, you may have to decide to stop drinking completely as the only practical way of eliminating the trouble.

The reason these decisions are so important, unlike a decision to use or not to use chewing gum or soda pop, is that alcohol is easily and too frequently abused. When people abuse soda pop, they usually get sick. Very few, however, abuse it, and when they do, the trouble they cause themselves and others is not very great.

Alcoholic beverages are different. The use and abuse of alcohol have led to all kinds of serious problems, both for the drinker and for the general public. We have not so far, in America, integrated the use of beverage alcohol successfully into our culture.

The variety of the remedies proposed for the problems, the wide range of the evaluations put upon our drinking customs, the extremes of con-

demnation and approval, make it difficult for the individual to arrive at sensible decisions about his own use of alcohol. The pressure to do what the crowd is doing, or to do what is expected by parents or friends or companions, make it all the harder to decide.

[Countless Americans are somewhat misinformed and confused about their drinking.] They cannot make a sensible decision whether to start drinking, or to stop drinking, or whether their drinking is moderate or dangerous, or even alcoholic, because the materials on which to base such a decision are not readily available to them. They need facts and principles.

Scientific facts are not a sufficient basis for decisions about human conduct. Principles of evaluation are required in order to make reasonable, human estimates of the bad, the good, the better thing to do. Hence this book, in addition to the basic scientific facts, sets forth basic spiritual and moral principles about the uses and abuses of drinking.

Decisions about drinking are very personal. You have to make them yourself. The theme of this book is: Decide for yourself about drinking, but do it on the basis of facts and principles.

CHAPTER 2

Some Scientific Facts

———•—•———

ALCOHOLIC BEVERAGES

THERE ARE MANY different kinds of alcohol. The kind used or produced in alcoholic beverages is called ethyl alcohol. Pure ethyl alcohol, straight alcohol, is not a beverage. It is too strong and unpleasant, and causes a harsh, burning sensation in the mouth.

There are two kinds of alcoholic beverage, fermented and distilled. The principal fermented beverages are wine and beer. The principal distilled beverages are whiskey, rum, brandy, gin, cordials, and liqueurs. Wine is much stronger than beer, and distilled beverages are very much stronger than wine, usually at least twice as strong as the strongest wine. Whiskey is ten times as strong as beer.

The Fermentation of Wine. When a fruit juice containing sugar, grape juice for example, is kept

standing in a warm place, microscopic yeast plants enter from the air, from the skin of the grape, or are added by the manufacturer, and chemical reactions take place. The sugar is changed to alcohol, and carbon dioxide is formed and bubbles away. This is the same gas that is added to soda pop to make it fizz. This process is called fermentation. The resulting product is wine, which may contain naturally anywhere from 10% to 16% alcohol.

The wines of lower alcoholic content, which are less sweet, are called *dry* wines, for example, claret, sauterne, chianti. The *sweet* wines, such as port, sherry, muscatel, have a higher alcoholic content, and in addition are frequently *fortified*, that is, alcohol is added to them, bringing their alcoholic content up as high as twenty percent or even higher.

If the wine is bottled before fermentation is complete, the carbon dioxide does not all bubble away but remains in the bottle. The result is a *sparkling* wine, like champagne or sparkling burgundy. Most wines are bottled after fermentation is complete and are called *still* wines. Sometimes imitation sparkling wines are made by charging still wines with carbon dioxide, the way soda water is made. Wines are also classified by their color,

white or red wines, and by their place of origin, Bordeaux, Rhine, California, Malaga, etc.

The Brewing of Beer. Beer is made from grain. Malt is used to convert the starch in the grain to sugar, because fermentation will not take place without sugar. Yeast is added to bring about the fermentation, as in the case of wine, and alcohol and carbon dioxide are formed. Hops are added for flavor.

In brewed beverages, fermentation is not allowed to go on to completion, and the average alcoholic content of beer in the United States is about four and one-half percent. Some of the carbon dioxide is retained when the beer is bottled or kegged. This is what gives the beer its fizz.

Ale is a heavier and stronger type of brewed malt beverage, but the difference between ale and beer is not as great nowadays as it was in years past. Beers that are made with larger amounts of cereals and extracts, and which consequently come out a darker color, are often called stouts or porters.

Distilled Spirits. Natural fermentation will not result in an alcoholic content above 14% to 16%. Higher concentrations of alcohol can be produced

by *distillation* of the product of fermentation. In this heating process, the more volatile alcohol is concentrated in the vapors, which are then condensed to a liquid of higher alcoholic content, while most of the water remains in the kettle. Distilled spirits usually contain 40% to 50% alcohol. "Eighty proof" means 40% alcohol (by volume); 100 proof means 50% alcohol, etc. When alcohol is made from grain, the resulting beverage is called whiskey; when made from sugar cane, rum; when made from wines or fruit juices, brandy. Gin is a mixture of alcohol, water, and flavoring material, including the juniper berry from which gin gets its name. Cordials and liqueurs are made by adding sugar, syrup, and flavoring to the alcohol. Although wine and beer are as old as history itself, the use of distilled beverages is a comparatively recent development. Brandy from wine was produced for the first time in France in the twelve hundreds, and the art of distillation was not in common use in Europe until about the year 1500.

Alcohol, the Significant Ingredient. It may sound superfluous, but it is the alcohol that counts in alcoholic beverages. The taste of these beverages would not account for their popularity if there were no alcohol in them. Furthermore, the flavor

of the alcohol itself is not particularly attractive to the majority of users. The alcohol is significant because it has *an effect* which is pleasant to most people, at least up to a certain point. The alcohol is the distinctive and all-important ingredient that makes these beverages popular, and at the same time gives rise to the problems of excess.

STATISTICS ON DRINKERS AND DRINKING

It is estimated that between 60 and 80 millions of people in the United States use alcoholic beverages at least occasionally. They pay about nine billion dollars a year for them, not counting the amount paid for bootleg liquor. This means that about two-thirds of our people who are of drinking age, that is, fifteen years or older, drink at least occasionally.

A recent survey of college drinking, based on a questionnaire answered by 17,000 students, shows that three-fourths of those questioned, both men and women, drink at least occasionally. In some colleges it appears that more than ninety percent of both men and women students drink. Four-fifths of the male students and two-thirds of the

women report that they started drinking before entering college.

The amount of alcohol consumed is hard to determine. The survey definitely indicates that the proportion of college students who drink heavily and frequently is very small. As for the general public of drinking age, we have estimates of the *apparent* per capita consumption of beer, wine, and spirits based on the taxes paid. It is called apparent consumption because there is no way of knowing accurately how much bootleg liquor is consumed. The amount of bootleg beer and wine is not thought to be very great at present, but the quantity of bootleg liquor may be half as much again as that on which taxes are paid. According to figures based on the taxes paid, the United States consumes somewhat less absolute alcohol per capita of drinking age population than it did 100 years ago, considerably less than it did 50 years ago, much more than it did immediately after prohibition, and about the same as it did 10 years ago. These figures also show a tremendous shift from hard liquor to wine, and especially to beer, in the last one hundred years. During the past ten years there has been a continuing shift to beer, especially packaged beer, much of which is consumed

in the home. This seems to indicate a change in our drinking habits and customs.

As compared with certain other countries, the United States ranks high in the consumption of alcohol (per capita of the drinking age population). The following list of countries is arranged in the order of their apparent consumption of absolute alcohol in recent years: France, Italy, United States, Belgium, Switzerland, Canada, Denmark, United Kingdom, Sweden, Ireland, Netherlands, Norway, Finland. But before drawing any conclusions from such a list, it is necessary to know how much of the alcohol is consumed in the form of hard liquor, how much as beer and wine, how much is consumed per capita of the *actual drinking population,* under what conditions of frequency and quantity, and many other factors.

Among those countries for which we have statistics, the United States stands second in the number of alcoholics proportionate to the population aged twenty years and over. The following list is arranged in the order of the prevalence of alcoholism: France, United States, Sweden, Switzerland, South Africa, Chile, Canada, Denmark, Scotland, Norway, Australia, Finland, Ireland, Northern Ireland, England, Wales, Uruguay, Netherlands, Italy, Belgium, Brazil, Spain, Argentina, Italy,

which consumes much more alcohol per capita than the United States, has only about one-seventh as many alcoholics.

In 1952 there were 400,000 known or suspected cases of tuberculosis in the United States, and this situation was recognized as a public health problem of serious proportions. But there were 4,000,-000 or ten times as many alcoholics in the United States at that same time. In addition, it has been estimated that there are millions of excessive drinkers whose excess causes problems for themselves and families, but whose problems have not yet become severe enough to class them as alcoholics.

WHY PEOPLE DRINK

Why do sixty to eighty million Americans pay nine billion dollars every year for alcoholic beverages? They must get something, or think they get something out of it. Otherwise they would not spend the money. In fact, why have countless millions of people from the very dawn of history used alcoholic beverages in one form or another?

Answering these questions can easily lead us away from the realm of scientific fact into the

realm of scientific or personal opinion, but some of the reasons for drinking are fairly clear.

The first and most universal reason for drinking is pleasure or enjoyment. Moderate drinking of alcoholic beverages gives most people a pleasant feeling of well-being, of euphoria. It makes them feel good.

In the course of history, alcoholic beverages have frequently been used ceremonially in connection with religious rites.

There are many people who drink because they like the flavor of certain alcoholic beverages.

Others drink because alcoholic beverages are a customary part of their regular meals and are considered important for dietary reasons.

In the past, alcoholic beverages were frequently prescribed for medicinal reasons. This is done much less frequently today because almost all the medicinal effects attributed to alcohol can be produced as well, if not better, by other means.

Many people still use alcohol to "cure a cold," under the mistaken idea that it will do so. It has no such curative effect. It may make the patient more comfortable, or help him to sleep better, but sometimes the cold is an excuse for drinking a little more than would be considered proper without the cold.

Many others drink because it is the thing to do socially, or because it provides an opportunity for association with convivial companions, or because it acts as a social lubricant, or is a traditional part of a social ceremonial, such as drinking a toast.

Teen-agers often drink because it gives them standing or prestige with their companions. They do it "to belong." Often they do it because it is considered a manly or grown-up behavior, and they want to be members of that adult world in which drinking is such a common custom. The mistake many teen-agers make when they drink for this reason is that they imitate those adult drinkers who never really grew up, who still drink in a childish search for excitement, and whose drinking behavior is a sign of their retarded emotional development.

The motivation of an alcoholic's drinking is a special problem, with many obscurities, and it will not be discussed here. Many of them drink *for escape,* but to explain all alcoholics in this way is an over-simplification.

Others drink to reduce physical discomfort, or to reduce mental anxiety. They find that drinking will relieve tension and help them relax.

STIMULANT OR DEPRESSANT?

The last-mentioned reason is very significant, because the most fundamental and universal reason for drinking alcoholic beverages is undoubtedly *the effect* of the alcohol when it gets into the blood stream. Alcohol in small amounts has a mild sedative and relaxing effect which is pleasant to most people. This is its natural physiological effect. Physiologically it is not a stimulant, according to the experts; it is a depressant or narcotic, and will put anyone to sleep if taken in sufficiently large amounts.

On the other hand, alcoholic beverages in small amounts frequently have an exhilarating or stimulating effect, which is also pleasant to most people. A workman, tired after a long day, experiences a lift or a pick-up when he takes a drink. People at a party become brighter and livelier after taking a drink. How can this be explained if alcohol is a depressant? There is a psychological explanation. After alcohol enters the blood stream, it affects the higher brain centers first, and depresses or sedates them. As a result, inhibitions are released and animal spirits, which would otherwise be held in check, are allowed to display themselves. Perhaps alcohol dulls the *consciousness* of those little aches

and pains that cause that tired feeling. The matter is by no means clear, but, whatever the exact nature of the explanation, scientists now seem to be in agreement that, physiologically, alcohol acts as a depressant, although psychologically it may often act as a stimulant.

The experts tell us that from the physiological point of view, alcoholic beverages are not sexual stimulants, nor do they directly cause sexual feelings or arouse sexual desires. But here again, it is a matter of daily experience that the drinking of alcoholic beverages, particularly when it is somewhat excessive, is often accompanied by sexual excitement. This is especially true in the case of young people and when young people drink in mixed groups. The explanation here also seems to be psychological. Alcohol depresses reason, judgment, and conscience, and the lower appetites assert themselves. Whatever the explanation, it is an indubitable fact that Bacchus and Venus have always been friends.

In speaking here of the effects of alcohol, I have dwelt principally on the *mild* sedative effect, or the *slightly* exhilarating effect of *small* amounts. If this is all that is meant by "feeling one's drink," there is nothing improper about it. Just as some people take coffee or tea as a stimulant or pick-up

and experience a feeling of well-being as a result, many other people take alcoholic beverages in moderate amounts and experience a mild pick-up or mild relaxation.

It is quite a different thing, however, to drink for the more exciting and violent effects, to drink to the point of getting high, or tight, or drunk. This means some stage of intoxication and more will be said about it later.

ALCOHOL IN THE BLOOD STREAM

The *effect* produced in people by drinking alcoholic beverages, not only the physiological effect, but also the psychological effect, depends on the concentration, that is, the proportion of alcohol in the blood. Alcohol goes into the stomach like other foods. Unlike other foods, however, it requires no digestion and passes directly through the walls of the stomach and small intestine into the blood stream, which carries it throughout the body. It is absorbed and diluted by all the fluids of the body, and obviously forms only a very small proportion of the total fluid in the body.

Nevertheless, a concentration of more than five one-hundredths of one percent (0.05%), one part in two thousand, will have some noticeable effects

on most people; and a concentration of fifteen one-hundredths of one percent (0.15%), three parts in two thousand, will be enough to make most people intoxicated. When the concentration reaches four-tenths of one percent (0.4%), even the most experienced drinkers will pass out. At one-half of one percent (0.5%), there is danger of death from deep anesthesia. No one, man or beast, survives seven-tenths of one percent (0.7%). When the concentration reaches this point, and often sooner, the nerves that control breathing are paralyzed and the person dies of asphyxiation.

It is a mistaken idea that alcohol in the blood stream directly irritates or damages the tissue, the seminal glands, the brain cells, etc. Scientists can find no evidence that the drunkenness of either or both parents at the time of intercourse or conception has a directly damaging effect on the sperm, the ovum, or the newly formed life. The alcohol never reaches a high enough concentration to do this kind of damage. But strong whiskey (e.g. 50% alcohol) will sting when applied to sensitive tissue, and may irritate and inflame the membranes of the throat or stomach by direct contact. Obviously, habitual heavy drinking by the parents will have a bad effect on the children, at least indirectly.

Rate of Absorption. Alcohol begins to be absorbed into the blood stream as soon as it reaches the stomach, although the greater part of the alcohol is absorbed only when it reaches the intestines. It is absorbed more slowly if the stomach is full. People sometimes eat butter to slow up the effects of drinking, but for this purpose, contrary to popular belief, bread, meat, and milk are more effective than fats. Excessive drinking on an empty stomach will make a person drunk more quickly than excessive drinking on a full stomach, but a full stomach will not prevent a person from becoming drunk if he continues to drink.

Rate of Oxidation. The body begins to oxidize or burn up alcohol from the moment it reaches the blood stream. Oxidation is a chemical process which starts in the liver. It goes on at a regular, fixed rate and cannot be hurried. It takes a certain amount of time for each individual, and if more and more alcohol is drunk, the body cannot oxidize it as fast as it enters the blood stream, and it accumulates or concentrates there. The rate of oxidation depends partly on the size of the liver, which in turn corresponds roughly to the size of the person. A large man (approximately 200

pounds) oxidizes the alcohol in one jigger of whiskey in about an hour.

FACTORS AFFECTING
CONCENTRATION OF ALCOHOL

The actual concentration of alcohol in the blood stream at any given moment, therefore, will depend on several factors:

1. *The amount of alcohol in the drink.*
   An ounce of whiskey has ten times as much alcohol as an ounce of beer, but of course beer is not drunk by the ounce.
2. *The length of time during which the alcohol is drunk.*
   If a single drink is nursed for an hour or two, the alcohol will be oxidized about as fast as it is absorbed and will not accumulate in the blood.
3. *The amount of food in the stomach.*
   The beverage itself may contain food elements which slow up the absorption of its alcoholic content. This is true of wine, and more so of beer.
4. *The weight of the drinker.*
   Other things being equal (which they rarely are) a person weighing 200 pounds will have to take twice as much alcohol as a person weighing 100 pounds in order to produce the same concentration of alcohol in the blood.

ALCOHOL CONCENTRATION AND DRUNKENNESS

One should not make the mistake of thinking that there is any absolute, exact correspondence between the percentage of alcohol in the blood and the states we call drunkenness, intoxication, or tipsiness. Most people would act quite drunk at three-tenths of one percent (0.3%), and anyone will lose consciousness at a concentration of four-tenths of one percent (0.4%).

Some people show signs of tipsiness with a rather low concentration of blood alcohol, yet others can carry a rather high concentration without giving outward signs of drunkenness. This is probably because the state of intoxication depends on many psychological factors as well as on the percentage of alcohol in the blood stream. Some people can learn by experience not to show the effects of drinking until they have taken considerable amounts.

Most excessive drinkers will exhibit signs of being high, tight, and drunk, in that order. But there are some who never show their drinks until they "fall flat on their faces." Consequently, when drunkenness is described in terms of the use of reason, the control of one's behavior and emotions,

there is no exact correspondence between the percentage of alcohol in the blood and the degree of drunkenness in the behavior. Furthermore, the same individual may react differently at different times to the same amount of alcohol in his system. These facts are well known even if the reasons for them are not entirely clear.

TOLERANCE

It is also clear that scientists cannot discover a physiological tolerance to alcohol which is comparable to the tolerance produced by the regular use of drugs. A person who takes a drug (e.g. morphine), builds up a tolerance for it, so that it takes larger and larger amounts of the same drug to produce the same physiological effect. This is not true of alcohol, at least not to any comparable degree. Some drinkers, however, seem to acquire a psychological "tolerance." They learn by experience how to take larger amounts, within limits, and not show it by any obvious signs of intoxicated behavior. On the other hand, it is also observed that alcoholics, who in the earlier stages of their alcoholism seemed to have an increasing capacity, in the later stages are seriously affected and made drunk by small amounts of drink.

LEGALLY UNDER THE INFLUENCE

Although there is no exact correspondence between the percentage of alcohol in the blood and the degree of intoxication, many people can be correctly described as under the influence of liquor (and the ability to drive a car is impaired considerably in most people), with concentrations ranging from over five one-hundredths of one percent to fifteen one-hundredths of one percent (0.05% to 0.15%) or one to three parts in two thousand. Over fifteen one-hundredths of one percent (0.15%), many people can be fairly described as intoxicated, even though not altogether drunk.

Because of these facts, some legal and medical authorities are in favor of fixing these amounts as somewhat arbitrary standards for courtroom purposes. Those whose blood shows 0.05% or less are presumed to be sober, with more than 0.05% up to 0.15% they are presumed to be under the influence, and with more than 0.15% they are presumed to be intoxicated. Some courts actually make use of these standards after the police have determined the percentage by one or other of the testing devices, such as the alcometer. (However, there may be a constitutional problem of forced

self-incrimination involved in the use of some of these methods.)

The reason why somewhat arbitrary standards are fixed at all is the immense loss of life and limb on our highways due to drunken driving. There is also the great practical difficulty of getting legal evidence and a conviction without resorting to presumptions based on percentage of blood alcohol. When laws are passed making such presumptions legal, the result is that those who drive when they have more than 0.05% alcohol in their blood may be held responsible even if not intoxicated.

How Many Drinks Make 0.05%? How much drinking does it take to raise the blood alcohol above 0.05%? It depends on many circumstances. A man of average weight (approximately 154 pounds) who drinks one highball, one cocktail, or two bottles of beer, on an empty stomach, even if he drinks it all down at once, will not produce a concentration above 0.05%. He could drink twice these amounts on a full stomach without going above 0.05%.

If the same man drinks two highballs or two cocktails on an empty stomach, the concentration may reach a maximum slightly above 0.05% but will fall to this level or below inside an hour. After

three highballs, it takes two or three hours to fall to 0.05%; after four highballs, 5 to 6 hours; after five highballs, about eight hours. But note again, since it bears repetition, that a concentration of 0.05% does not necessarily imply tipsy behavior or an appearance of partial intoxication. Sometimes it does, often it does not. It does imply, however, a slowing up of reaction time and other depressant effects which make a person driving an automobile a poorer risk. The drinker himself may be the last to recognize these effects because of the deceptive influence of the alcohol.

EXAGGERATIONS

Sometimes exaggerated statements are made about the physiological effects of alcohol.

> "Alcohol is a poison."
> "Drinking is bad for one's health."
> "Drinking shortens life."
> "Alcohol causes the brain cells to deteriorate."
> "Drinking is good for one's health."
> "Drinking increases one's strength and vigor for hard labor."
> "Moderate drinkers live longer than abstainers."

Each of these statements needs correction or qualification. Moderate quantities of alcoholic

beverages are not poisonous. Even when moderate amounts are drunk regularly, there is no scientific evidence that it is bad for one's health or shortens life. We have already seen that the concentration of alcohol in the system is never high enough to do direct damage to brain cells or to other tissue. On the other hand, the drinking of alcoholic beverages offers no positive contribution to good health that cannot be supplied by other and better means, and does not increase one's strength and vigor. As for long life, there is no evidence to show that moderate drinkers live longer than abstainers, or vice versa, although these statements are sometimes made by propagandists.

ALCOHOL AS FOOD

Alcoholic beverages generally have high caloric values. A jigger of whiskey contains about 100 calories, a bottle of beer about 190 calories, and a bottle of ale about 225. A three ounce glass of port wine has about 150 calories, and of dry sauterne, about 75 calories. But the alcohol calories in these drinks, unlike the calories of fats and carbohydrates, can be used only as fuel. They are burned to produce energy, cannot be stored for future use, and cannot repair or build up tissue.

Hard liquors have very little food value in addition to the alcohol they contain. Whiskey, for instance, is more than ninety-nine and one-half percent water and alcohol. Beer and wine contain more food elements of a useful kind. Alcohol itself has none of the vitamins or minerals that are essential to bodily health. Hence, it is a very poor food, and a bad substitute for other foods.

EXCESSIVE DRINK AND DISEASE

The excessive use of alcohol, however, does lead to various body ailments. In the first place, heavy drinkers and alcoholics generally neglect other food. A person who gets half his calories from alcohol over a period of a week may have considerable energy, but, because of the serious deficiency of vitamins and minerals, he may become severely ill. The same vitamin deficiency accounts for some of the so-called diseases of alcoholism, such as beri-beri and pellagra. Cirrhosis of the liver occurs in heavy drinkers and alcoholics many times more frequently than it occurs in the general population. It is a mistake, however, to think that all cirrhosis of the liver is due to alcoholic excess.

Scientific research has not shown that alcohol is a direct cause of liver damage, stomach ulcers, tu-

berculosis, cancer, or kidney diseases. But heavy drinkers often neglect hygiene and diet, and are in poor physical shape, so that when disease comes along, they are easy targets.

Heavy drinkers and alcoholics are also subject to *delirium tremens,* a frightening and dangerous seizure which is never experienced by non-drinkers. Death as a direct result of drinking ethyl alcohol is rare because a person usually loses consciousness before the danger point is reached and can therefore drink no more. But, if he is already close to the passing-out stage and drinks a pint or more of undiluted whiskey quickly, he can raise the concentration to the point where the nerves controlling his breathing are paralyzed, and he will die of asphyxiation. Long-continued, excessive drinking, in conjunction with bodily and/or personality factors, often results in alcoholism, about which more will be said later. Excessive drinking is an important factor contributing to the deaths of many men and women. Although no one knows the exact annual count, the number is large.

DANGEROUS DRINKING

People who are just beginning to drink, those who drink infrequently, and those who have

learned to drink with true moderation are in no immediate danger of physiological ill-effects. But they should be aware of certain dangers which, for many people, are connected with any kind of drinking.

There is the obvious danger of going on to excess and becoming intoxicated, with all that that may entail. Young people and those who drink in search of excitement and thrills run special risks in this regard. As we shall see, drinking is no longer moderate when one uses it to produce exciting and violent effects.

They should also be aware that, even short of intoxication, drinking slows up reaction time and interferes with mechanical skills and sensory powers. One of the commonest fallacies in the world, which has been scientifically disproved many times, is: "I can drive better after I've had a few drinks." Furthermore, the effect of alcohol is sometimes unpredictable, so that one cannot be sure ahead of time how great its effect will be.

The use of alcohol to bolster up morale, to escape from boredom or loneliness, to make up for personality defects, to overcome shyness, to soothe mental pains and anxieties, involves still more subtle dangers. Alcoholic beverages often give temporary relief in these situations, but the relief

is delusive and is not a real solution of the problem at all.

Alcohol in these settings seems to be a friend and ally; but it is an ~~insidious~~, false friend, because this type of drinking easily leads to dependence on alcohol and finally to addiction itself. The master's crutch then becomes the master's master.

THE BASIS OF A PERSONAL DECISION

The foregoing scientific facts about alcohol have not been stated to convince you either to give up drinking or to take up drinking. The object has been to supply you with information so that you can make a sensible decision of your own about your drinking. In order to make such a decision, you need scientific facts.

But you need more than mere scientific facts; you need spiritual principles. The following sections will give you spiritual and moral principles concerning the use and abuse of alcoholic drinks.

CHAPTER 3

Practicing the Virtue of Sobriety

VIRTUE AND SELF-DISCIPLINE

"PRACTICING VIRTUE" seems like a rather old-fashioned and pious phrase, but the word virtuous originally meant "befitting a man." It remains true today that the only way we can act like human beings, the only way we can reach the goal that God has set for us, is by practicing virtue.

Our appetites for food, drink, and sexual indulgence are naturally strong and naturally blind. If left to themselves they can easily lead us to destruction. They are not subject to reason as they should be. Because of original sin, man's lower nature, the law of his members, is in rebellion against his higher nature, the law of his mind. It is only through arduous self-mastery that we can subject our appetites to the control of reason. Our parents began to teach us self-discipline, especially in eating and drinking, almost from the time we were infants. The practice of Christian self-denial in imitation of Our Lord is a means of achieving

self-discipline and self-control. Without these we cannot be virtuous.

Mere self-denial is not a virtue in itself. In itself it is often sterile, unconstructive, and frustrating. But self-denial for a supernatural motive, as a means to the practice of virtue, and as a means of following in the footsteps of Our Lord, is one of the basic principles of Christian spirituality. No Christian can do without it.

Spiritual Athletes. We have to exercise ourselves spiritually, like athletes training for a contest, in order to practice virtue. St. Ignatius, in his little book of the *Spiritual Exercises,* begins with his famous *Principle and Foundation:* "Man was created to praise, reverence, and serve God, Our Lord, and thereby save his soul. And the other things on the face of the earth were created for man's sake, and to help him in the following out of the end for which he was created. Hence it follows that man should make use of creatures so far as they help him toward this end, and should withdraw from them so far as they are a hindrance to him in regard of that end."

Beverage alcohol is one of those "other things on the face of the earth," a creature which man should make use of so far as it helps him, and with-

draw from so far as it hinders him in his journey back to God. It is not one of those things that is in itself forbidden to the liberty of our free will, such as stealing or lying.

Alcohol is neither morally good nor morally bad; it is morally indifferent, or morally neutral in itself. But since it is a creature extremely attractive to sense appetite, it is dangerous.

Men become easily attracted to such creatures and run the risk of fastening their hearts upon them, sometimes even preferring the creature to the will of the Creator. Such preference is sin. It means following animal instincts instead of acting like a human being. It means giving up the practice of virtue.

Temperance and Sobriety. The virtue which regulates man's appetite for the pleasure of food, drink, and sex is called *temperance* by theologians. It is not concerned merely with drinking alcohol.

Temperance is a "cardinal" virtue, that is, one which has many parts or sub-divisions. Chastity is that part of temperance which regulates the appetite for sexual indulgence. Abstinence is that part of temperance which regulates the appetite for ordinary food and drink. Sobriety is that part of temperance which regulates the appetite for strong

drink, i.e. beverage alcohol. A special virtue is needed for the regulation of this appetite, St. Thomas Aquinas tells us, not merely because beverage alcohol is so attractive to the sense appetite, but because the abuse of it so quickly attacks man's reason and judgment, first diminishing it, then eliminating it.

There are two ways of practicing sobriety, just as there are two ways of practicing chastity. One way is by moderate use, the other by complete abstention. Some people practice the virtue of chastity by giving up the use of sex entirely. If they do this out of Christian self-denial and for the love of God, as priests and Sisters do, it is exceedingly virtuous. Others practice chastity by getting married and living chastely while making use of sex within the married state. They, too, are practicing virtue.

It is somewhat the same with sobriety. Some practice it by total abstinence from alcoholic beverages for a supernatural motive. Others practice it by making use of these beverages, and keeping their use within the bounds of moderation, also for a supernatural motive. (The word "temperance" itself means moderation, primarily, rather than total abstinence. To identify temperance with total abstinence is a comparatively recent American usage.)

It is now necessary to explain a little more fully the meaning of moderation in drinking. The next chapter will explain total abstinence from drinking.

MODERATION IN DRINKING

How can you determine what is meant by moderate drinking? It would be impossible to establish a definite daily ration of alcohol (wine, beer, or spirits) which would be a moderate amount for everybody. It would be like trying to assign a definite quantity of food as a measure of moderation, beyond which anyone would be guilty of gluttony.

People differ so widely, and circumstances vary so greatly, that any such attempt is doomed to failure. For some individuals one drink is always immoderate, in accordance with the saying: "For an alcoholic one drink is too many and a thousand are not enough."

Nor can one measure moderation by the concentration of alcohol in the blood, for example, by saying that over 0.05% is always immoderate. Again, this would be like trying to measure the sin of gluttony by the number of calories a person has eaten during the day. Different people are affected very differently by the same concentra-

tion, and the same person is affected differently at different times. Furthermore, the circumstances can change the picture completely. Drinking a certain amount before going to bed might be moderate, while drinking the same amount before driving a car would be immoderate.

Moderation in drinking must also take into account such things as expense. If you or your family cannot afford what you are spending on alcoholic beverages, your drinking is immoderate, even if it leaves you completely sober. If your drinking interferes with your family obligations, business affairs, or whatever other duties you have, it cannot be called moderate. If your drinking is an occasion of sin for you, for example, causing you to commit sins of impurity, that also is immoderate.

Examples of Moderate Drinking. Here are some examples of drinking that are well within the bounds of moderation.

A family is accustomed to drink wine at dinner as an ordinary part of the meal. They like the taste, it is their national custom to use wine in that way, and they consider it a useful part of their diet. Even the children get a little wine mixed with water.

A working man is accustomed to drinking a bottle or two of beer every day, perhaps one when he gets home from work and another with his evening meal.

Another family serves cocktails before dinner. Some members take one and others take two.

A neighbor who entertains a bridge party serves two or three highballs in the course of the evening.

These drinkers all derive pleasure from their drinking. They experience pleasures of the sense of taste, a mild lift, or a comfortable sense of relaxation, a mild euphoria.

These examples of regular use, considered in themselves and apart from modifying circumstances, would be called moderate by anyone who believed that drinking was permissible at all. There is certainly no gluttony here, no exaggerated indulgence in the sense-pleasures of eating and drinking. If these people "need" a drink in the evening, they need it much as they need coffee in the morning, or a cigarette after dinner, or a cup of tea in the middle of the afternoon. Their need does not amount to a dependence on alcohol.

No Dependence on Alcohol. If they had a real dependence on alcohol they would not be satisfied for long with these quantities. The dependent

drinker who really needs alcohol as a crutch to help him overcome shyness, or anxiety, or to gain self-confidence, or because he can't stand life, or because everything gets on his nerves, is a poor risk where alcohol is concerned. His drinking may be externally moderate for a time, but his motives are not moderate, well-ordered, and temperate.

Such motives make drinking particularly dangerous. These drinkers are very likely to increase the amount they take, and to depend on alcohol more and more as time goes on. Alcohol offers no real solution to their emotional problems. It is just a pain-killer that covers and complicates the problems without doing anything constructive about them. This emotional dependence is another sign that the drinking is immoderate.

No Violent Effects. In the foregoing examples, there is no thought of intoxication, no desire or intention of getting high, much less tight. No one would think of such drinking in terms of violence: "slugging it down," or "getting a jolt out of it." There is no search for excitement and thrills, no looking forward to a "high old time" or a "real binge of a party" or a "bit of a wild time," with liquor the all-essential ingredient of the fun and excitement. In fact, the drinking provides only a

mild kind of pleasure and relaxation, is taken for granted as a pleasant adjunct, and nobody gives it a second thought.

What is Drinking For? Now someone will probably ask: "But what is drinking for if you don't drink to get a jolt or a kick out of it? Two or three drinks don't do anything for me—they only tease me. You don't call that really drinking, do you? What becomes of the party spirit? What becomes of all the fun and excitement and hilarity?"

These questions are typical of many American users of alcoholic beverages. They betray a fundamental misconception as to the real purpose of beverage alcohol. One would expect younger drinkers, perhaps, to think along these lines. One would understand, at least, that youthful exuberance leads them to experiment with everything, and most of all with excitement.

In our country, however, a great many people of mature age still maintain a somewhat immature attitude about drinking. They drink in order to get high or tight because they really think that is the thing to do. So many otherwise respectable people drink in this excessive way, that it becomes the socially acceptable thing to do in some circles. The result is that we have developed a dangerous

frame of mind and some dangerous drinking customs. Many people are so accustomed to the idea of drinking more or less excessively, that they react in surprise and resentment when anyone suggests that this is *not* what drinking is for, and that such drinking is immoderate.

Why are these drinking customs and this frame of mind dangerous? It is not at all unlikely that one of the reasons we have such a high rate of alcoholism in this country is that so many people drink for the more violent effects. It is easier, of course, to get these effects from hard liquor, and so we use a great deal of it in comparison with some of our European neighbors.

But apart from the dangers of future addiction and alcoholism, this kind of drinking frequently includes the danger of drunkenness and all the evils that go with it. Later on, when violations of the virtue of sobriety are discussed, we will give reasons why drinking to get high and tight is immoderate, and why it is not in accordance with the virtue of sobriety.

Then what is drinking for? "Wine was created from the beginning," says the Bible, "to make men joyful, not to make them drunk" (Ecclesiasticus 31:35). Joyful means cheerful, not hilarious. The theologians who say that drinking is permitted in

certain circumstances *usque ad hilaritatem,* mean
the same thing. The Latin word *hilaritas* means
cheerfulness, not hilarity.

Drinking has various legitimate uses, but one of
the most important seems to be the effect of mild
relaxation, or mild exhilaration, or cheerfulness,
which it provides for most people who take alcoholic beverages in small amounts. The drinkers
who think that this mild effect is not worth having
or bothering about are often the poorest risks with
a full glass in their hand.

Abstinence Obligatory? There are some students
of drinking problems who are at the opposite ex-
treme, who are so impressed by the abuses of beverage alcohol that they think any drinking at all is
immoderate and that everyone should be a total
abstainer. They say that we owe it to our weaker
brethren who cannot handle alcohol to give them
good example; or they say that the danger of future addiction is so great that no one is justified in
running the risk of drinking at all.

This is not the place to defend moderate drinking against the charge of sinfulness. It is enough
to point out that moderate drinkers also give good
example by their very moderation, even if this
good example has not the same dramatic quality

is total abstinence. As for the danger of future addiction, it is true that no total abstainer, who remained a total abstainer, ever became an alcoholic.
However, it is equally true that no moderate
drinker, who remained a moderate drinker, ever
became an alcoholic.

Life would not be livable if we always were
obliged to abstain from an action because we foresaw in it the possibility of future evil consequences. If that were the case, no one could go
pleasure-driving on a Sunday afternoon, because
statistics show clearly that pleasure-driving results
in many fatal accidents, even when all the parties
concerned are perfectly sober.

The Christian and Pleasures. Our Lord Himself
practiced the virtue of sobriety perfectly, and He
was not a total abstainer. The tantalizing problem
for His sincere followers, whether or not they use
alcoholic beverages, is to draw the line in their
own individual lives between a legitimate indulgence of the pleasures of this life, and an excessive,
pagan pursuit of pleasure. This problem, Christian self-denial versus pagan pleasure-seeking, can
arise from dancing, candy, amusements, sports,
table delicacies, coffee-drinking, or any one of the

numerous pleasures which the modern world makes so readily available.

It was only a few hundred years ago that the devout priests of a certain religious order in Europe protested bitterly against the introduction of coffee at breakfast. They maintained it was expensive, luxurious, imported and exotic, not in keeping with religious poverty, and not befitting men dedicated to God. They insisted on retaining their traditional breakfast beverage, which was beer.

Nobody has yet defined exactly what moderate drinking is for each individual case. It is a very personal, almost delicate matter which you will have to decide for yourself with the light of God's grace. But the above examples and considerations should help you recognize some things that moderate drinking *is not*. If you keep them in mind, they will help you answer the question: "Is my drinking truly moderate? Is it befitting a human being, a child of God, and a follower of Christ?"

CHAPTER 4

Total Abstinence from Drinking

TOTAL ABSTAINERS do not necessarily think they are giving up something bad in order to do what is good. They give up something *good*, the moderate, virtuous use of beverage alcohol, in order to do something *better*. This second way of practicing the virtue of sobriety is called total abstinence.

It was not easy to explain moderation in drinking, but it is easy to explain total abstinence. It means just what it says: not drinking any beverage (beer, wine, spirits, or cordials) that contains alcohol. This abstinence is practiced for a supernatural motive, such as penance, self-denial, good example, reparation to Our Lord for sins of intemperance, safeguarding sobriety, etc.

THE PLEDGE

Many of those who practice total abstinence take a pledge to do so. This pledge is a promise, made

from religious motives, not to drink any alcoholic
beverages for a certain period of time, or for life.
It is not a vow, which always means a solemn
promise to God which binds under pain of sin. As
the pledge is given nowadays, it is a sacred resolution, but the violation of it does not in itself con-
stitute a sin.

Contrary to widespread belief, the principal use
and the principal usefulness of the pledge is not to
reclaim drunkards. The pledge is taken much more
frequently (in Ireland, for example, by the Pio-
neers) by those who have no personal problem with
drink, but who wish to offer up to God acts of self-
sacrifice for spiritual reasons like those given
above. Taking the pledge is often one of the membership requirements of a total-abstinence organization. These societies are usually social organiza-
tions, too, which, in addition to offering their
members a spiritual challenge, provide them with
opportunities for recreation and social gather-
ings.

There is a mistaken idea that all total abstainers
are prohibitionists. This is by no means universal-
ly true of total abstainers in the United States. A
great many of them favor "moral suasion" in promoting the practice of the virtue of sobriety by total abstinence, and do not favor prohibitory laws.

TOTAL ABSTINENCE PURITANICAL?

Another false idea current among many Catholics in this country is that total abstinence is a puritanical or Protestant ideal, and that there is something slightly un-Catholic about it. This is not true. The idea is due probably to the fact that some Protestant denominations take the position that total abstinence is obligatory on all Christians, and many of them have been vigorous crusaders for absolute legal prohibition.

Actually, however, the Catholic total abstinence movement, in this country and elsewhere, has had the highest approval of the Church and her theologians. Leo XIII, writing to the United States in 1887, encouraged both clergy and laity to participate in this work: "We esteem worthy of all commendation the noble resolve of your pious associations by which they pledge themselves to abstain totally from every kind of intoxicating drink. Nor can it at all be doubted that this determination is the proper and truly efficacious remedy for this very great evil; that so much more strongly will all be induced to put this bridle upon appetite by how much the greater are the dignity and influence of those who give the example."

People are puzzled by this notion of total absti-

nence. First they are taught it is not a sin to drink. Then they are taught that truly moderate drinking can be virtuous. Then they are encouraged to be total abstainers, even from the virtuous use of drink. Is this logical?

It would not be logical, of course, to say that moderate drinking is permissible and then say that total abstinence is obligatory on everyone. But this is not our position. Total abstinence is not a precept binding the conscience under pain of sin. It is more like a counsel, or an invitation to do something extra for the love of Christ. People often give up something for Lent out of a spirit of penance or self-sacrifice. What they give up is not something sinful, but something permissible, like going to the theatre or eating candy. They give it up to practice self-denial in imitation of Christ; they do it to show that they want to give God not only the minimum of service which He demands under pain of sin, but they want to make a sacrifice, a gift of something extra. They do not give up something bad in order to do what is good. They give up something good in order to do what is better.

A Better Way. The practice of total abstinence is adopted for similar reasons. The true follower of Our Lord wants to do great things for Him. How

mean and spiritless would we be if the entire measure of our devotion to Christ were: "Is it a sin or not? If it is not a sin, and gives me pleasure, I will do it."

Accordingly, many followers of Christ choose total abstinence because for them it is a better and more perfect way of practicing sobriety. But it cannot be said that this would be the more perfect way for everybody. Our Lord certainly practiced the virtue of sobriety to the most perfect degree, as He did all other virtues, and He was not a total abstainer.

Given the circumstances of the society in which we live, given the immense abuses of excessive drink, and given the need of good example to strengthen the weak, the practice of total abstinence becomes a peculiarly appropriate way of practicing and safeguarding the virtue of sobriety here and now. As Leo XIII said, it is the "proper and efficacious remedy for this very great evil." It is also a very appropriate means of making reparation to Christ for the many sins of intemperance by which He is offended.

The fear of future addiction is sometimes stressed as a motive for practicing total abstinence. Since there is a very real danger of future addiction for many people in this country, this is also a sen-

sible reason for choosing total abstinence. The to
tal abstainer who remains a total abstainer wil
never become an alcoholic, and so the practice is ar
excellent method of *safeguarding* the virtue of so
briety and preventing alcoholism. But it should
also be noted that over-emphasis on this motive is
not very effective, because most people just do no
believe that they will ever become alcoholics. Be
sides, the fear of addiction is not nearly so high and
challenging a motive as generous self-sacrifice in
the following of Our Lord.

Pressure on Young People. Total abstinence is a
challenge. It is especially challenging for young
people, who are peculiarly susceptible to the pres
sures of the circles in which they move, and are
anxious to have the approval of their companions
to belong, and to be part of the gang. They ask, for
instance, if they will miss some of the fun if they
do not drink as the others do. The answer is yes
they will miss some of the fun but also a lot of the
grief. What value would total abstinence have as
self-sacrifice, as a generous gift to God, if you do
not miss anything?

Or they ask: "Isn't it better to learn how to drink
when I am young, so that I will become accus
tomed to it and know how to drink properly when

I am older?" "Isn't it better to learn to drink at home, rather than to do it outside on the sly?" It certainly is better to learn to drink at home, *if* you have already decided to drink.

But it is a fallacy to think that there is any necessity of learning to drink at all. It is entirely in the luxury class. Nobody needs to learn in order to be successful and happy in this life, or prepared for the next. There are a good many, sad to say, who have to learn how not to drink in order to reach God.

Bad Manners. Another thing that bothers younger people is that it seems rude to refuse a drink when it is offered. The person who is really rude is the host or hostess who urges alcoholic beverages on a guest, or who serves only alcoholic beverages, thereby leaving the guest no choice.

A host should realize that there are millions of people for whom one drink is poison, and should respect the preferences of those who, for one reason or another, have decided not to drink. *It is always extremely rude to force a drink on anyone.* It is equally unmannerly to call attention to what a guest eats or drinks, or to imply that one who does not drink must be a puritan, or a strange type, or

some kind of weakling who cannot take his drinks like a man.

These are the attitudes with which young people and others are frequently faced when they decide to exercise their right to drink or not to drink. Anyone who chooses total abstinence should be prepared to run his own life in spite of these pressures. Those who are interested in promoting the practice of sobriety will have to exert what influence they can to eliminate these thoughtless and immature attitudes from American society.

COMPATIBLE IDEALS

In the past there has often been a certain amount of opposition between those who crusaded for total abstinence and those who defended the moderate use of alcohol. The teetotalers at times gave the impression of being holier than thou. The others gave the impression at times of having very generous ideas of what came under the heading of moderate drinking.

Some exponents of total abstinence have been vigorously opposed to any drinking whatever, even the truly moderate kind. Some drinkers have displayed considerable resentment to the least suggestion that they are drinking a bit immoderately.

The unfortunate consequence has been to divide people into two opposing camps, the teetotalers and the drinkers; the "teetotalers" standing for severity and extremism, while the term "drinkers" unfortunately carries with it the implication of immoderate self-indulgence. The result has been a blurring of the distinction between truly moderate drinking and the prevalent drinking customs of our country, especially the drinking of hard liquors, which encourage, or at least find socially acceptable, a use of alcohol which ranges from somewhat immoderate to downright excessive.

Would it not be possible for the exponents of total abstinence and of moderate use to come to terms on the common ground of Christian sobriety, a virtue which may be exercised both by abstainers and drinkers? There is no intrinsic reason why two social-religious movements, one for total abstinence and one for virtuous moderation, should not work side by side as friendly allies in a common cause. There are no contradictory principles involved which would make the two movements natural enemies.

Why would it not be possible to have an *organization* for the promotion of Christian sobriety which combined both these ideals? All its members would be pledged to the practice of sobriety, but

it would be left to the individual to decide whether he would choose abstinence or moderate use. Each would respect the other's preference and neither group could claim that it had chosen the "holier state in life." The more perfect choice would more often be total abstinence, but not always, and it would be the private, personal affair of each one what choice he had made. The organization could also include recreational and social programs for the different age groups. But it would rely primarily on supernatural motives and supernatural means, especially prayer and the sacraments. Such an organization already exists in Europe.

CHAPTER 5

Violating the Virtue of Sobriety

THE VIRTUE OF SOBRIETY is violated by the sin of drunkenness or intoxication. When we speak of people as being high, or tight, or drunk, we mean increasing degrees of intoxication. Being high or tight corresponds to what the theologians call partial intoxication. Being drunk, or actually passing out, corresponds to what the theologians call complete drunkenness or complete intoxication.

Intoxication means something more than that pleasurable feeling of mild relaxation or mild exhilaration and cheerfulness which are the natural consequences of moderate drinking. Again it is a question of degree, and there is no sharp dividing line between the legitimate stage of pleasurable indulgence and the sinful stage of partial intoxication. Neither is there a dividing line, clear and sharp, between partial intoxication and complete intoxication. The various stages shade off into one another.

This does not mean we can never say for sure whether a person is high or not, or drunk or not. In the spectrum, orange shades off into red by imperceptible degrees. One part of the spectrum is clearly and definitely red, and another part is clearly and definitely orange. Some people are clearly drunk, often for some time before they pass out. And some are quite clearly high or tight, beyond the bounds of sobriety, though not completely drunk.

HIGH, TIGHT, DRUNK

Some examples may help to clarify this. At a social gathering or party where most of the guests are taking a drink or two, one man is drinking more than the others. His face is flushed. He is talking louder, faster, and probably sillier than usual. A joke that evokes a smile from the others gets a guffaw from him. His reactions are impulsive and his perceptions are fuzzy. People would say he is tipsy, or under the influence, or mildly intoxicated. He is high. (Probably, if his blood alcohol were taken it would be over 0.05%; but some get high on less than that, and others do not get high on more than that.)

Take the same man an hour or two later. He is

still drinking. Some of the psychologically exhilarating effects of alcohol are now wearing off and its depressant physiological effects are becoming more apparent. He stumbles over his speech. He sways in his walk. He may be ready for a fight for no good reason, or may make some foolish amorous attempt in a clumsy and rather senseless way. He may see double, or be nauseated. But he still knows where he is and what he is doing. His conversation is still pretty rational, though his perceptions are even more clouded and fuzzy. He is tight.

Still later in the evening, if he keeps on drinking, this man will become completely drunk. He will hardly know what he is doing. He will not be able to exercise reasonable control over himself and over his ordinary physical activities. He will not be able to navigate, or respond to the reactions of others. He may say or do things that are completely foreign to his normal character. Probably tomorrow he will not remember even the principal things that happened to him during this part of the evening. He is drunk.

Deliberate drunkenness, whether partial or complete, has always been condemned as immoral by Christian theologians. But one is not guilty of sin unless one deliberately intends to drink excessively, and to become at least partially intoxicated. Ac-

cidental drunkenness is another matter. It would not be sinful either, to drink deliberately to the point of intoxication if it were necessary for some serious medical reason, for example, if no other anesthetic were available. But deliberate drunkenness for motives of self-indulgence cannot be excused in this way.

REASONS WHY DRUNKENNESS IS WRONG

Christian theologians appeal first of all to Holy Scripture to show that drunkenness is sinful. "Nor drunkards . . . shall possess the kingdom of God," says St. Paul (1 Cor. 6:10). And the Fathers of the Church, together with the common tradition of civilized peoples, have condemned drunkenness as immoral.

First of all, excessive drinking is often a form of gluttony. Just as greedy over-eating is unsuitable to man as a rational being, so also is greedy over-drinking. The expression "to make a pig of oneself" gives the common estimate of mankind that this greediness is something less than human, and is out of keeping with the dignity of a man and a follower of Christ. To the extent that excessive drinking means an exaggerated indulgence of ap-

petite, an abuse of the sense of taste, it is gluttonous and therefore sinful.

In the second place, and much more fundamental, a man deliberately and without necessity deprives himself of the use of reason, to a greater or lesser degree, by drunkenness. This use of reason is the greatest gift of God to man, and it is the mark that distinguishes man from the rest of visible creation. To extinguish deliberately and violently or dim notably the light of reason is a kind of self-mutilation.

Christians do not believe that man is master and owner of his own body and mind, to do with as he pleases. He is a steward, who is obliged by the terms of his stewardship to take care of his own health as the gift of God, to respect the integrity of his physical members as the property of God, and, above all, to preserve intact his own reason, lest he destroy within himself the image of God.

Hence the excuse of some excessive drinkers: "It is my own affair whether I get drunk or not. I hurt only myself, and that's my own business." That excuse is invalid. Man is not at liberty to do as he likes with his own life, his own health, and his own reason. It is not permissible for a human being to make himself incapable of acting like a human being. Besides, drunkenness in a Christian

is a degradation of the temple of the Holy Ghost.

It is interesting to note that some theologians treat of drunkenness, especially habitual drunkenness, under the commandment "Thou shalt not kill." The Fifth Commandment, besides forbidding murder and self-destruction, is taken to forbid self-mutilation and to command a reasonable care of one's own life and health. There is also a psychological appropriateness in considering drunkenness a kind of suicide. Especially for the alcoholic, each cup has a little death in it, a little of that oblivion which he seeks, consciously or unconsciously.

When drinking is excessive, and especially when excess is habitual, there frequently are present other factors which contribute to its immorality. For instance:

> The intolerable situation imposed on wife, husband, or children.
> The harm to which one exposes self and others.
> The damage to family and friends.
> The waste of needed money.
> The acts of impurity.
> The acts of dishonesty.
> The blasphemies.
> The fighting.
> The drunken driving.
> The traffic accidents.
> The scandal, especially to children.

The unemployment.
The poverty.
The disgrace.
The danger of addiction.
The broken health.
The broken home.

Some or all of these very frequently result from drunkenness, even from partial drunkenness. When excess is habitual, some of these evils are inevitable. Whole sermons could be written on each one of them. It is enough to say here that they are additional reasons why drunkenness is immoral.

RESPONSIBILITY FOR ACTS
WHILE DRUNK

People often ask whether they are guilty of the things that happen when they are drinking—things they would not have done if they had not been drinking, for instance, sins of impurity, or fighting, or automobile accidents, etc. If they foresee that any of these things are likely to happen, and deliberately go on drinking regardless of consequences, they are guilty. If they do not foresee them, then their guilt depends on how much control they had left when they did them.

A man may be tight and still sufficiently in

charge of himself to be guilty of sin. Individuals differ greatly in this regard. Some people drink excessively just in order to be bold enough to commit sin. They cannot avoid responsibility in this way.

The general rule is that a person is not guilty of the acts committed while completely drunk unless he foresaw the likelihood they would happen, and was deliberately willing to go ahead and take a chance that they would happen. In such a case he is guilty of them in the sight of God, whether or not they actually happen.

Serious Sin. So far we have explained what is meant by drunkenness, partial and complete, and the reasons why it is sinful and immoral. The question then arises, when does one commit a serious sin in this regard, and when a venial sin?

It is clear from both Scripture and Tradition that habitual, voluntary drunkenness is seriously sinful and excludes from the kingdom of Heaven. This is the minimum meaning of St. Paul's statement, quoted above, and theologians have always been in agreement on this point.

Nowadays authorities on moral theology teach that a single deliberate act of complete drunkenness is always seriously sinful. A person who know-

ingly chooses to deprive himself completely of his power of reasonable control over himself is always guilty of serious sin on that account, and may also be guilty because of one or more of the additional reasons enumerated above.

Sometimes people start drinking without intending to go so far, and become drunk through inexperience or an unpredictable accident. They are not then guilty of grave sin. At other times people set out to get drunk and even to stay drunk for a while—to "tie one on." This conduct is always gravely sinful.

To get tight deliberately is often seriously sinful because of the many evils connected with this kind of heavy drinking, especially when it is habitual; but in itself, and apart from all such consequences, a single act of partial intoxication is only venially sinful.

To get high deliberately is also at times a serious sin because of the evils connected with it and the circumstances in which it occurs. In itself—*per se,* as the theologians say—getting high is a venial sin.

THEOLOGICAL MISCONCEPTIONS

In this country, owing to the widespread custom of drinking hard liquors precisely for their more

violent effects, many people are unwilling to accept the idea that drinking to get high is *per se* venially sinful. They think they have a right to drink that way. They think that is what drinking is for.

One reason for this misconception is the oft-quoted phrase from the moralists, that it is permissible at times to drink *"usque ad hilaritatem."* This is mistranslated as "to the point of hilarity." It really means "to the point of *cheerfulness."*

Another reason is the abuse of the somewhat odious expression "theologically drunk," which means "completely drunk" as the theologians understand this term. The abuse consists in taking for granted that there is no sin, at least no serious sin, committed as long as one is not completely drunk.

The truth is that there is often serious sin in lesser stages of intoxication because of the various connected evils. This is especially true when heavy drinking is frequent or habitual. In any case, to get high deliberately is far from complete or "theological" drunkenness, and yet it is a venial sin which offends God.

Why Wrong to Get High? Either or both of the following reasons explain why this kind of drinking is not in keeping with man's dignity and vio-

lates the stewardship he should exercise, in the name of God, over his person and his faculties. First, to get high generally involves gluttony, an excessive indulgence of the pleasures of taste and appetite. The quantity required to make most people high, if they are at all experienced in the use of alcoholic beverages, is sufficiently large to lay them open to the charge of over-indulgence of the appetite. Such gluttony is venially sinful.

Secondly, getting high means partial intoxication, a partial loss of the use of reason. It is equivalent to a minor mutilation of reason and judgment. It noticeably impairs the drinker's control over his human activities. As a steward entrusted with the keeping of a body which should be the temple of his reason as well as the temple of the Holy Ghost, he has no right to take such liberties. There can be no doubt that a person who is high in the sense we have described suffers considerable impairment of function, good judgment, memory, self-control, reaction time, and physical coordination.

These are the reasons why drinking to get high is in itself venially sinful, apart from all the accompanying and consequent evils that may sometimes make it seriously sinful, such as squandering money needed for family care, seriously endangering one's own life or that of others on the highway, etc.

TURNING THE MIND TO GOD

These distinctions between serious and venial sin have not been proposed in order to show people how far they can go without committing sin, or how far they can go without committing grave sin. That kind of negative thinking inevitably leads downhill and away from God. It ends in serious sin.

The purpose has been simply to explain the truth of these matters as it is proposed by the theologians so that each one can apply these principles to his own conscience and his own conduct. In matters of this kind, no one can point out to another exactly where sin begins for him, and just exactly where grave sin begins. We each have our own conscience, which is the voice of God. If we consult it honestly, with these principles in mind, and ask God to enlighten us, we need have no fear of offending Him.

Actually the excessive drinker sins against himself, too. He sins against the love he should have for himself. Our Lord told us to love our neighbor as ourselves. It is not selfish to love oneself. That instinct is deep in human nature and is natural to it. It is selfish to love oneself too much.

The excessive drinker, although it is hard to

convince him of it, is his own worst enemy. The sin he commits against well-ordered self-love has its inevitable repercussions on the love of neighbor. Then the undue attachment to the creature, drink, inevitably means turning away from the Creator, God. St. Thomas says that drunkenness is immoral because it prevents the mind from being turned toward God. Fundamentally that is why Christian teaching condemns deliberate drunkenness as immoral.

CHAPTER 6

Alcoholism

THE DECISION to stop drinking is all-important for the alcoholic. It is a very hard decision to make, but it is his only salvation. Many people, whose drinking has become a real problem, do not know that they are alcoholics, and frequently do not even recognize that their drinking is the chief cause of their troubles. It is a fact that, whether the troubles drove them to drink or the drink complicated the troubles and made new ones, the troubles will never begin to straighten out until they do something about the drinking.

The following observations about alcoholism may help a problem drinker to understand what the scientific world means by alcoholism today, and help him to decide whether he should consider himself an alcoholic. They may also prove useful to the general public, especially to the family in

which alcohol is causing trouble, by providing some understanding of alcoholism, and some information on how to help the man or woman who has become a victim.

DESCRIPTION OF ALCOHOLISM

It is a commonplace boast of the alcoholic in the earlier stages that he can take it or leave it. But he always takes it. The truth is that he can neither take it nor leave it. He cannot take it with impunity and he cannot leave it without help.

Hence the complaint of the alcoholic in the later stages: "I can't live with it and I can't live without it." This is the interior contradiction that drives him to despair.

The conflict within him is not merely that struggle of the law of the mind against the law of the members of which St. Paul speaks. This is the common lot of all men. To the alcoholic it is a struggle and a conflict that has assumed pathological proportions.

A habit of self-indulgence can and often does degenerate into addiction. When addiction has set in there is a new problem. It is no longer the problem of mere drunkenness. It has become the problem of alcoholism.

Alcoholism vs. Drunkenness. Alcoholism is not the same thing as drunkenness, nor even the same thing as excessive drinking, or excessive drinking over a long period of time. There seem to be certain people who are able to drink too much over long periods of time without becoming alcoholics. However, proportionate to the amount and frequency of their excess, they are in grave danger of becoming addicts.

Judged by the world's standards, they do not get into serious life problems and serious trouble with their drinking. If they are called upon to give up drinking and are given strong enough reasons for doing so, they can give it up by themselves; not easily, but with much less difficulty than the addict. They have not seriously injured their health or their family, or their business or social relationships. They can give it up much as the man with a long, strong habit can give up smoking if he wants to. It is a difficult thing to do, but he does not have to call in the doctor, the priest, the psychiatrist, and the A.A.s in order to be able to do it.

Alcoholism is not just plain drunkenness. It is drunkenness plus—plus serious life problems due to drink, and plus addiction.

The alcoholic is the person whose excessive

drinking creates serious problems in the manage-
ment of his life, and yet who is usually unable to
stop drinking for good, even if he wants to, with-
out outside help.

Excessive drinking means getting drunk frequently, or at least getting good and tight frequently over a period of years. The serious problems
range all the way from disruption of family harmony to complete deterioration of the individual.
Typical problems are: intolerable home conditions
caused by drinking, loss of job, loss of family, loss
of health, loss of moral ideals, loss of faith, loss of
self-respect, commitment to jails, mental institutions, etc.

The inability to stop drinking implies addiction.
When the alcoholic seriously tries to drink moderately he always fails. His firm resolution to take
only two drinks this time collapses and melts away
almost as soon as he has tasted the liquor. When
he tries to stop drinking altogether, he may suc-
ceed for a time on his own, on the strength of his
good resolutions. But generally these resolutions
turn out to be jelly. The solemn pledge, sincerely
taken, is soon broken. The lamentations and ex-
hortations of those he loves the most are of no avail.

He is suffering from a compulsion to drink, a

compulsion that hits him at various times with more or less frequency and more or less force. He needs help to overcome it. The kind of help he needs to escape from his bondage may be medical, psychiatric, social, religious, or a combination of all of these. One of the reasons for the large-scale success of Alcoholics Anonymous is that it combines many kinds of help and offers them to the alcoholic in a way that he can accept.

When these three elements are all present together, excessive drinking, serious life problems, and inability to stop unaided, it is safe to say that the drinker is an alcoholic in the sense in which that word is used by scientific authorities today. When any one of these three elements is absent, the classification of the individual as an alcoholic is questionable.

Frequent Misconceptions. There are certain misconceptions about alcoholics. People think of an alcoholic as a derelict on skid row, but this is far from typical. There are 4,000,000 alcoholics in the United States, and not 10% of them are on skid row. The vast majority still live at home, in a family (or on a family), and the majority still work, not very efficiently, perhaps, but they still have a

job. Alcoholics are drawn from all classes: rich and poor, educated and uneducated, skilled and unskilled, men and women. There are probably four or five times as many men alcoholics as there are women alcoholics in this country. Most alcoholics are between the ages of thirty-five and fifty-five.

It is also a mistake to think that all alcoholics are continually in a state of complete drunkenness, or at least get drunk every chance they get. There are a good many of them who become completely drunk rather infrequently, but they do get tight, thoroughly and often.

Another false idea is that a man who can hold his liquor, that is, one who has the capacity of drinking a great deal without showing it a great deal, will not become an alcoholic. The man who boasts that he can drink the other fellow under the table and then see that he gets home safely, and who never has a headache in the morning, is actually just as dangerous a drinker, if not more so, than his friend with the weak stomach or the weak head. If and when he does become a victim, he will be as powerless over alcohol as any other alcoholic. It is impossible to predict which heavy drinkers will become victims.

Most alcoholics in the advanced stages do not

care for the taste of whiskey. Their craving for it is not a desire to experience a pleasant taste, nor is it a sensation of thirst. It is a deep need, difficult to explain and hard to understand. It becomes more and more compelling as the alcoholism makes its insidious progress. An alcoholic once said: "At first I drank because I wanted to; then I drank because I needed to; finally I drank because I *had* to." Alcoholics say that only an alcoholic can fully appreciate that craving, and what the word alcoholism really means.

It is commonly thought that a person who can give up drinking for Lent is not an alcoholic. This is one of the most frequent mistakes about alcoholism. Thousands upon thousands of recovered alcoholics have given up drinking altogether, but they are still alcoholics because they are only one drink away from a drunk. *The test is not the ability to stay away from it, but the ability to take it regularly in moderation.* A person who can take two or three drinks and no more, regularly, is not an alcoholic. No alcoholic can do that *with regularity* over any considerable period of time.

It is an exaggeration, therefore, and bad tactics, to tell a problem drinker or a suspected alcoholic that all alcoholics get drunk every time they take

a drink. Even if he is a real alcoholic, he can probably recall, like many alcoholics, a good many in-
stances even in his recent drinking career, when he
was able to take a few drinks and get away with it.
Therefore he will conclude that he is not an alcoholic. It is the memory of those occasions which
foster in the mind of the alcoholic the illusion that
perhaps he can learn to handle it all the time; the
false hope that he can learn to drink always in the
controlled way he does on certain occasions. This
hope is only a delusion. As stated previously, compulsive, alcoholic thinking operates at various
times with more or less frequency and more or
less force, and the alcoholic can never predict on
which occasions it will operate. Hence, he can never predict what will happen if he takes only one
or two drinks. An alcoholic is a person who cannot
safely drink at all.

The Only Solution. Consequently, for an alcoholic there is only one way of practicing the virtue
of sobriety and that is by total abstinence. In that
struggle of his to recapture the pleasures of other
days, when he could drink normally, he has not a
chance. His everlasting tussle with himself to learn
how to drink like other people, or to drink just
enough to keep feeling comfortable, is absolutely

foredoomed to failure. His only hope is to surren
der wholeheartedly to this idea: "I can't handle i
any more and never can. Drinking is not for me.'

SELF-DIAGNOSIS

This is a shattering prospect for a person who
does not know how to live happily and contented
ly without liquor. Therefore the act of surrender,
the sincere admission of defeat, is sometimes post
poned for years, when it has become all the harder
to learn to live without it. One reason is that the
drinker has all those misconceptions about alcoholism in his mind: he is no derelict; he can still
drink his friends under the table; he has a job and
a family; others drink just as much, if not more,
and nobody calls them alcoholics; he can go on the
wagon for Lent, etc. How, then, can anyone call
him an alcoholic?

Problem drinkers in this frame of mind have
sometimes profited by an honest study of the following check list of the progressive symptoms of alcoholism. It is a list of behaviors which hundreds
of alcoholics have reported about themselves, and
which have been observed by those who have had
wide experience with alcoholics.

The behaviors are arranged roughly in the chronological order in which they occurred during the drinking careers of these alcoholics, most of whom, unfortunately, reached the late chronic stages of alcoholism before they really understood what was happening to them, gave up, and recovered. There is no record of any single alcoholic having gone through all the behaviors on this list. And the behaviors have not occurred in exactly this order in any individual case.

Often a behavior that is typical in the later stages, will occur by way of exception in the earlier stages, but these are the things that alcoholics have actually done and are doing. These are the things that happen as a person goes through the progressive stages of alcoholism. These behaviors form a typical pattern.

A person who goes through this list and checks off, with complete honesty, each and every behavior he has experienced in connection with his drinking, may gain some new knowledge about himself and his drinking. He may discover that he is following a typical pattern of alcoholic drinking and thinking; that the things happening to him are in fact the progressive symptoms of alcoholism. An alcoholic is a fortunate man indeed if he can

recognize this and admit it sincerely without hav
ing to go through the agonies of the later stages.

CHARACTERISTIC BEHAVIORS
OF ALCOHOLISM

1. *Preliminary Stage:*

  Frequent excessive drinking, not necessarily
    complete drunkenness (this continues
    throughout all the stages).

  Alcoholic beverages unusually interesting and
    satisfying.

  Increasing number of drinking episodes.

  Drinks more at each episode.

  Extra drinks before party.

  Sneaking drinks.

  Drinks to feel at ease with others, or at a dance,
    etc.

  Blackouts (not a loss of consciousness but a
    temporary loss of memory—can't remember
    what happened).

  Gulping first drinks.

  Guilty feelings about drinking habits.

  Avoids conversation about alcohol.

  Reacts defensively to mention of alcohol.

  Proportion of **Blackouts** to drinking episodes
    increases (an ominous sign of oncoming al-
    coholism) .

N.B. Some excessive drinkers seem to remain in the preliminary stage and do not go on to become alcoholics. Others stay there for many years and then become addicts.

2. *Early Stages of Alcoholism:*

Frequent excessive drinking.

Increasing amounts.

Loss of Control After a Few Drinks (inability to drink moderately is the beginning of addiction).

Extravagant or grandiose behavior (phone calls, treating, taxis, gifts).

Reproached by family and friends.

Makes home life unhappy.

Rationalizes excessive drinking (alibis, self-delusion, lies).

Drunken driving.

Humiliates wife or husband in the presence of others.

Neglect of sacraments or prayer, or both.

More efficient after one or two drinks.

Solitary Drinking.

Loses time from work through drink.

Financial difficulties due to drinking.

Narrowing range of interests.

Loss of ambition.

Protecting supply, by hiding bottles, etc.

Morning Drink (to get over the effects of previous day's excess).

Needs more liquor to get same effect.

Reputation affected.

Indifferent to kind of beverage alcohol.

Neglect of family's welfare.

Moral deterioration becomes noticeable.

Changes pattern of drinking (only wine, only beer, etc.).

Goes on wagon (for Lent, for months, for year, for life).

Tries taking pledge.

Anti-social acts (aggressiveness, arguments in taverns, etc.).

Frequently misses Mass or Church.

Walks out on friends (thinks friends stuffed shirts, snobs, etc.)

Friends walk out on drinker.

Refuses to talk about his drinking, resents any mention of it.

Resents boss unreasonably.

Walks out on job unreasonably.

Geographic escape.

Loss of jobs.

Drinking becomes of central importance.

Seeks medical advice, or psychiatric advice.

Persistent sleeplessness.

Neglect of food while drinking.

Week-End Benders.

Hospitalization because of drinking.

Pills (barbiturates).

Marked self-pity (everybody down on me, etc.)

"What's the use" attitude.

3. *Advanced Stages of Alcoholism:*

Little or No Control (often called a hopeless
drunk).

Gets drunk on less liquor.

Persistent, nagging remorse.

Drinking any kind of alcohol (shaving lotion,
vanilla extract, etc.)

Progressive moral deterioration.

Loss of faith.

Unpredictable benders.

Arrests and imprisonment.

Persistent tremors (which continue after the
binge and the hangover).

Diminishing sex potency.

Vague, indefinable fears.

Raging, unreasonable resentments.

Alcoholic psychosis.

Delirium tremens.

Rum fits (convulsions).

Hallucinations.

Bankruptcy of alibis and rationalizations.
Suicidal attempts.
Involuntary commitment to various institutions.
Skid row.
Insanity.
Death.

A DISEASE OR A MORAL PROBLEM?

One of the most frequently discussed questions about alcoholism is this: "Is it a disease or a moral problem?" Probably the best way to answer this question is to say that it is both. Certainly it is hard to understand how anyone would go through all the agonies and heartbreaks of the list of characteristic behaviors and do it out of sheer obduracy. There is something pathological about drinking that goes on and on when it is so obviously contrary to the self-interest, well-being, and happiness of the drinker.

On the other hand, the alcoholic is by no means an insane or completely irresponsible individual. His conduct, then, involves problems of morality. This, too, is no less strongly indicated by the typical pattern of alcoholic behavior. A convenient way to express this complicated state of affairs is to

say that the alcoholic suffers from a triple sickness —a sickness of body, of mind, and of the soul.

Many alcoholics have contracted various diseases, for instance, cirrhosis of the liver, as a result of excessive indulgence. These are called the diseases of alcoholism. But when alcoholism is called a disease, it is meant that the abnormal drinking itself is a disease, or that the general disordered condition of the alcoholic should be called a disease or an illness.

This disease concept has not met with universal acceptance. First, it is impossible, at present, to identify a definite disease entity which all alcoholics have in common. Alcoholism is not like tuberculosis, diabetes, or the various heart diseases in this respect. Secondly, the disease concept is resisted by those who feel that this gives the alcoholic a good excuse to go on drinking and say: "I can't help it; I'm sick." It is also resisted by those who feel that the condition of alcoholism cannot be adequately described as a disease, since it involves behavior and misbehavior which are within the power of the alcoholic to control.

Why Called a Disease. On the other hand, justification is offered for referring to the abnormal drinking or the general disordered condition of

the alcoholic as a disease. First, the professions of medicine and psychiatry see in the alcoholic a condition which, by their norms, deserves to be called a disease. They are the judges of what the label "disease" means, and of whether the condition called alcoholism deserves that label.

Secondly, recovered alcoholics cannot learn to drink normally. After years of sobriety, they still react abnormally if they start drinking again. Why is this so, unless there is something inside them, physiological or psychological, which makes them react that way? That something is rightly called pathological.

Thirdly, some scientists believe they have discovered a physiological basis for the alcoholic's abnormal drinking. Although researchers in physiology have not as yet been able to agree upon a clear, definite, organic, or functional pathology in alcoholics generally, there is good reason for believing that the abnormal drinking in many alcoholics results from a bodily pathology; and that in most alcoholics, once they have become addicts, physiological changes have occurred which prevent them from ever becoming normal drinkers.

Fourthly, the psychological (and/or physiological) mechanisms involved in addictions, of whatever kind, can properly be called pathological.

Once the alcoholic becomes an addict, he has acquired a dependence on alcohol which is usually beyond his power to control, unaided. This addiction is often as strong as drug addiction, and, as an addiction, can be considered a mental illness or disease.

Accordingly, the sickness of the mind referred to here is not some neurotic or psychotic condition that may be the underlying cause which drives the alcoholic to drink. It is rather the addiction itself, the addictive or compulsive thinking.

Weak Willed? Many are under the impression that the typical alcoholic is a weak-willed person who simply has not the strength of character to say "No" to appetite. There are undoubtedly many weak-willed individuals among alcoholics, just as there are in the general population. But there are many strong-willed persons, too, whose wills are as strong or stronger than the next man's, *except in the case of alcohol*.

There are times when something happens to an alcoholic's thinking in regard to alcohol. For instance, after having had a few drinks, his consciousness and imagination narrow down to the thought of the next drink, which becomes the one, all-engrossing object of desire. He cannot think

realistically of anything else. All other things, including the excellent motives he has for not taking that drink, are either not in his mind at all, or are there only in a dreamy, far-off, unrealistic way. He says that the only real thing to him at that moment is the drink. This is what is meant here by compulsive or addictive thinking.

Moral Responsibility. The compulsion to drink does not take possession of an alcoholic at all times or whenever he thinks of alcohol. In the earlier stages of addiction it seems to happen quite regularly after he has had a few drinks. But in the later stages there are undoubtedly times when it happens to a man who has had nothing to drink for a long time.

It would also be an exaggeration to think that it always deprives the drinker of all responsibility for taking the drink. As mentioned above, the compulsion operates with more or less frequency, more or less force. Even non-alcoholics at times experience a similar fascination, but it does not have the same strength and persistence as in the case of the alcoholic. In all such matters, the question of pathology is a question of degree. Some place along the line the fascination is abnormal enough to be called pathological.

When a person is in the grip of this addictive or compulsive thinking, it is clear that his freedom and moral responsibility are considerably diminished insofar as the drinking itself is concerned. Of what use is it to say, "Give the alcoholic strong enough motivation and he will no longer drink." He usually has motives that would be absolutely compelling for anyone else. The sickness of mind consists in this: that even the strongest motives do not get through to him at those moments when he is in the grip of the addiction.

What good does it do to say to the alcoholic, "Use your will-power." His sickness consists in this: that his will-power, no matter how good it is for other things, is powerless over alcohol whenever that compelling fascination for alcohol takes possession of his mind.

The moral responsibility of the alcoholic for the drinking itself is not like that of other people. His responsibility for his excessive drinking is generally diminished to a considerable extent, and sometimes eliminated. But each alcoholic, each drinking episode, and even each act of drinking, must be judged separately.

The honest and enlightened testimony of the drinker's own conscience is the best criterion we have of his subjective responsibility. In the final

analysis, after making allowance for the pathological character of his addiction, judgment must be left to a merciful God.

Spiritual Sickness. In addition to the disorders of body and mind that are characteristic of the alcoholic's condition, many alcoholics go through a gradual process of moral and spiritual deterioration. The fibres of the alcoholic's character become weaker, and he regresses in his emotional attitudes and his moral outlook.

A great many alcoholics begin their drinking by way of harmless self-indulgence, but this indulgence soon becomes so attractive that it leads to sinful excess. Sins of deliberate drunkenness become habitual. Little by little one moral ideal after another is allowed to grow dim: honesty goes; humility goes; purity goes. There ensue: increasing selfishness and egocentricity; increasing self-deception; increasing neglect of family, business, and friends; increasing resentments and cynicism; neglect of the sacraments; neglect of Mass; finally, in many cases, a despairing rejection of Almighty God Himself. The lessons learned in childhood are disdained. What began as harmless self-indulgence, degenerates into addiction.

The alcoholic finds himself morally and spiritu-

ally bankrupt, at odds with God, at odds with his own conscience, and finally deprived of his own self-respect.

This is not true of all alcoholics by any means. But the gradual process of deterioration, for which they are responsible in varying degrees, is true of so many that it must be considered characteristic of the condition. This position has been confirmed by the experience of Alcoholics Anonymous, which has been more successful than any other agency in modern times in the large-scale rehabilitation of alcoholics. Their central program, the "Twelve Suggested Steps of Recovery" is a program of moral and spiritual regeneration. If this medicine of the soul is so successful in arresting alcoholism, it is fair to conclude that the alcoholic's sickness is, in part at least, a sickness of the soul.

A Triple Sickness. Alcoholism, accordingly, is not just a disease, and not just a moral problem. It is both. It is a sickness of body, mind, and soul.

The sickness of the body refers to whatever physiological factors scientists can point out as contributing to the abnormal drinking.

The sickness of the mind is the compulsive or addictive thinking which sometimes takes possession of the alcoholic with regard to drinking.

The sickness of the soul is the moral and spiritual deterioration characteristic of so many alcoholics.

HOPE AND HELP
FOR THE ALCOHOLIC

Although the alcoholic may be more or less powerless over alcohol and unable, at times, directly to resist the craving for drink, yet it is within his power, generally speaking, to do something positive about his drinking. Today there is new hope for the alcoholic because the kind of help and knowledge he needs has become more and more available to him.

Physical and Mental Help. On the physical plane, doctors are taking a new interest in alcoholism. General hospitals are beginning to open their doors. Aversion and antabuse treatments have achieved some success, but as yet, there is no such thing as a cure or a magic pill which will enable the alcoholic to learn how to drink in moderation.

A special word of warning is necessary against the use of sleeping pills by alcoholics. Since they are addictive personalities, they can easily become addicted to sedatives. They should use any kind of

sedation with great caution and only with the advice of physicians who are aware of the special
dangers that are present in such cases.

A further word of warning to families and associates of alcoholics: call a doctor. The acute alcoholic often requires competent medical care, even
hospitalization. It is dangerous to shrug off his condition by saying "Just drunk." That does not meet
the situation adequately.

On the mental plane, psychiatry has helped
many an alcoholic by teaching him how to live
with himself and to accept the fact that the only
solution for him is complete abstinence. Psychoanalysis has not been particularly successful.

Moral and Spiritual Help. On the moral and spiritual plane, pastoral counselling has been effective
in a great many cases. Alcoholism involves problems of human conduct and misconduct. No one,
no matter how well-balanced and virtuous, can
continue to practice virtue and please God unless
God helps him to do it by the gift of His grace.
The alcoholic, with his special problems, is particularly in need of that grace. The principal
means of grace are prayer and the sacraments.

The administration of the pledge, for short periods, and in cases where alcoholism is not too far

advanced, has also been recommended and found useful. But the more advanced the alcoholism, the less likely it is that the pledge by itself will be effective, for an advanced alcoholic makes a resolution which he is literally unable to keep without aid. The pledge, therefore, seems to have been more effective as a preventive of alcoholism than as a remedy.

Alcoholics Anonymous. A.A. has been very successful in restoring alcoholics to permanent and contented sobriety. Its program is in thorough harmony with Christian theological and ascetical teaching. It offers its members rough and ready emotional re-education, group therapy, sympathetic understanding and companionship, resocialization, practical assistance when the moment of temptation arrives, and introduces them to a new set of non-drinking friends and social activities. Another important part of the program is helping other alcoholics.

The fundamental tenets of A.A. are admission and acceptance of the fact of alcoholism, and reliance on the grace of God to achieve permanent and happy sobriety. The only requirements for membership are the admission of one's drinking problem and the desire to do something about it.

There are no dues, initiation fees, or solicitation of funds. The organization will not even accept any donations from those outside the membership. Its entire support comes from voluntary collections taken up at meetings of its own members. It has been far more effective in the large-scale rehabilitation of alcoholics than any other organization in modern times.

The central program of A.A., "Twelve Suggested Steps for Recovery," is as follows:

1. We admitted that we were powerless over alcohol—that our lives had become unmanageable.
2. We came to believe that a Power greater than ourselves could restore us to sanity.
3. We made a decision to turn our will and our lives over to the care of God as we understood Him.
4. We made a searching and fearless moral inventory of ourselves.
5. We admitted to God, to ourselves, and to another human being the exact nature of our wrongs.
6. We were entirely ready to have God remove all these defects of character.
7. We humbly asked Him to remove our shortcomings.
8. We made a list of all persons we had harmed, and became willing to make amends to them all.
9. We made direct amends to such people whenever possible, except when to do so would injure them or others.
10. We continued to take personal inventory, and when we were wrong, promptly admitted it.

11. We sought through prayer and meditation to improve our conscious contact with God as we understood Him, praying only for knowledge of His will for us and the power to carry that out.

12. Having had a spiritual awakening as the result of these steps, we tried to carry this message to alcoholics and practice these principles in all our affairs.

Today there are several thousand A.A. groups scattered throughout the United States. No city of any size is without at least one group. Many of them are listed in telephone directories under "A.A." or "Alcoholics Anonymous." If not, discreet inquiry will easily discover where they can be reached, or a card to the central Headquarters in New York will bring an immediate reply, in a plain envelope, telling you where you can contact the nearest group. The address is P.O. Box 459, Grand Central Annex, New York 17, N.Y.

The A.A.s are interested primarily in the individual alcoholic, not in the family of the alcoholic. When the drinker is ready to ask for help, they are always eager to give it to him—all he has to do is telephone.

In addition, they are often in a position to give good practical advice to the members of the family. They do not, however, consider this their primary job, and of course they do not pretend to be

able to make anyone stop drinking. But they can make valuable suggestions for handling the alcoholic until he or she is ready to ask for help. They also know the local resources and hospitals, the doctors who are interested in alcoholism, the clergymen who are well-informed and sympathetic, the state commissions and other agencies. Many distraught members of alcoholics' families have received hope, encouragement, and sound practical advice by contacting a self-sacrificing member of A.A.

Whether the alcoholic member of the family is father, mother, husband, wife, son or daughter, the other members need information, orientation, encouragement, and practical advice on how to behave in this extremely trying situation. Such advice cannot be attempted here, because it has to be adapted to the individual circumstances.

The National Committee on Alcoholism, Inc. This is the national clearing house for information on developments and activities in the field of alcoholism. It disseminates the latest scientific and medical findings in this field, and also guides and stimulates the establishment of community programs on alcoholism. Forty-nine local affiliates operate such programs. Literature is available from

the national headquarters at 2 East 103rd Street, New York 29, New York.

One of their functions is to give advice in situations of this kind and to supply literature that will help the alcoholic, the family and the general public to become better informed about alcoholism. A personal visit to one of these offices and an interview with a member of the committee will often be a source of great practical help to a member of the family in need of advice.

A particularly useful book for the same purpose is: *Primer on Alcoholism,* by Marty Mann (Rinehart, New York). It contains detailed suggestions for the various members of the family, telling them what to do and what not to do in order to help the alcoholic.

This varied help is becoming increasingly available to the alcoholic. But often the real problem is to get him to accept help of any kind. It will do no good to preach or scold. He or she often strenuously resents any pressure to visit a doctor, a priest, a psychiatrist or the A.A.s.

Unless the family realizes that the alcoholic is not a stubborn good-for-nothing, that, whatever his misdeeds, he is actually the victim of a pathological condition, they will make many mistakes in handling him. Their well-meant efforts will boom-

erang. The only effect will be an increase of his resentment and hostility, thus postponing the day
when he will "hit bottom," see himself as he really
is, surrender, and begin his recovery.

THE FAMILY'S CROSS

While the alcoholic is still drinking, the members of the family have a heavy cross to bear. Their
difficult situation, continuing month after month,
sometimes year after year, is bound to have its
effect on them. It becomes injurious to their
health, emotionally nerve-wracking, and destruc-
tive of all peace of mind. They are sometimes in
need of counsel and advice almost as much as the
alcoholic.

They need to have it explained that suffering is
not useless in the Christian scheme of life, and that
this very suffering, accepted with supernatural
submission to the will of God, can be the means of
ultimate recovery for the alcoholic as well as sanc-
tification for themselves. They need to be shown,
by concrete sympathy and priestly zeal, that there
really is hope and help for the alcoholic.

CHAPTER 7

Conclusion

———•—•———

YOUR DECISION

THESE SCIENTIFIC FACTS about alcohol, and these fundamental spiritual principles about the use of alcohol, have been presented to you as a basis for making personal decisions about your own life. Without the facts and the principles, you are in no position to decide what to do about drinking. But from the facts and principles set down, you should be able to do some clear-headed thinking about yourself and alcohol.

It would not do any harm either, to talk the matter over with some experienced person in whose good judgment you have confidence. Perhaps you will decide that not to drink at all is the best thing for you. Perhaps you will decide that your use of alcohol is as it should be. Possibly you will decide that your ideas on moderate drinking need revision. Perhaps you have discovered that you are getting too close to the area where alcoholism begins, or have even crossed over. If so,

there is only one sensible decision you can make.

A time of decision is like an important switch-point on the main line of the railroad. If the switch is turned properly, the train will travel hundreds of miles in the right direction. If it slows up at times, or even stops, it will always be headed in the right direction.

If you take the right turn on an important question of your life, and, with the help of God's grace, make that big decision a wise one, any number of smaller decisions will take care of themselves. No matter what mistakes you make afterwards—if you weaken, or slow down, or falter, or stop, or even slip back—you will always be headed in the right direction.

In order to choose the right direction you need not only human wisdom, but enlightenment from God. God gives us His grace in the form of enlightenment for the mind and inspiration for the will—but only if we ask for it. Pray for this grace as the Church prays for her people: ". . . that they may *see* what they should do, and have the strength to *do* what they have seen" (Prayer of the Sunday within the Octave of Epiphany).

Suggested References

BOOKS

Alcohol and Human Affairs. W. B. Spalding and J. R. Montague. World Book Company, Yonkers, New York, 1949. A high school textbook with a brief appendix on drugs.

Alcohol and Social Responsibility. R. G. McCarthy and E. M. Douglass. Thomas Y. Crowell Company and Yale Plan Clinic, New York, 1949. A general work on alcohol problems in the United States, with special reference to academic instruction on these problems.

Alcohol, Science and Society. Yale Center of Alcohol Studies, New Haven, Connecticut, 1945. Contains twenty-nine lectures on all phases of alcohol problems and alcoholism, delivered at the Yale Summer School of Alcohol Studies in 1945.

Alcoholics Anonymous. The Alcoholic Foundation, New York, 1951. This is the A.A. "bible," containing case histories of early A.A. members and the fundamentals of A. A., written by the founders and first members.

Depth Psychology, Morality and Alcoholism. J. C. Ford, S.J. Weston College Press, Weston, Mass., 1951. Contains two monographs, one on psychoanalysis and unconscious motivation, the other on the moral responsibility of the alcoholic, with extensive bibliographies on both topics.

Primer on Alcoholism. Marty Mann. Rinehart & Co., New York, 1950. Contains fundamental information on alcoholism and practical advice for the family on what to do and what not to do in dealing with the alcoholic.

Twelve Steps and the Twelve Traditions, The. Harper & Brothers, New York, 1953. An interpretation of the A.A. program by one of its founders, with special emphasis on the twelve suggested steps of A.A. as means to character formation by the alcoholic.

Articles and Pamphlets

"Alcoholism" (Catholic Encyclopedia, Suppl. II). J. C. Ford, S.J. The Gilmary Society, New York, 1953. A general article on alcoholism, moral responsibility, rehabilitation and prevention.

Alcoholism Is a Sickness. Herbert Yahraes. Public Affairs Pamphlets (No. 118), New York, 1946. Surveys the nature of alcoholism and the approach to it as a public health problem.

Facts About Alcohol. R. G. McCarthy. Science Research Associates, Inc., Chicago, Illinois, 1951. This is a *Life Adjustment Booklet,* suitable for high school and college study groups, and also for the general reader. An *Instructor's Guide* is available for classroom use.

Golden Book of the Spiritual Side, The, and several companion volumes. S.M.T. Publishing Company, Indianapolis, Indiana. Interpretations of the A.A. program written by a Catholic priest. A new booklet appears annually.

Introduction to A.A., and *A.A.—Questions and Answers.* The Alcoholic Foundation, New York, New York. These pamphlets, along with several others, are published by A.A. to introduce alcoholics and others to the work of the organization.

Lay Supplement Series. Yale Center of Alcohol Studies, New Haven, Connecticut. A series of twelve popular language pamphlets, prepared by a committee of the editorial board of the *Quarterly Journal of Studies on Alcohol,* and covering a wide range of topics in the alcohol field.

Shall I Start to Drink? J. C. Ford, S.J. The Queen's Work Press, St. Louis, Missouri. Spiritual motivation for total abstinence, addressed principally to younger people to help them decide for themselves.

13 Steps to Alcoholism: Which Step Are You On? Morris J. Weeks, Jr. J. F. McQuade, Inc., New York. A brief, graphic presentation of the progressive symptoms of alcoholism for the person who does not know what alcohol is doing to him. This pamphlet is also obtainable through the National Committee on Alcoholism, New York.

NATIONAL AGENCIES

Alcoholic Foundation, The, P. O. Box 459, Grand Central Annex, New York 17, New York. This is the Alcoholics Anonymous organization headquarters. It publishes A.A. books and pamphlets, and is the service center and clearing house for A.A. activities throughout the world.

Association for the Advancement of Instruction About Alcohol and Narcotics, 52 Hillhouse Avenue, New Haven, Connecticut. This organization assists public and private educators to inform students concerning alcohol and narcotics.

National Clergy Conference on Alcoholism, The, P. O. Box 1194, Indianapolis 6, Indiana. This group offers assistance to the Catholic clergy in their pastoral problems.

National Committee on Alcoholism, Suite 454, New York Academy of Medicine Building, 2 East 103 Street, New York 29, New York. Formerly the National Committee for Education on Alcoholism, this committee publishes pamphlets and educational material for the adult general public, and has affiliates in the principal cities of the United States.

Yale Center of Alcohol Studies, The, 52 Hillhouse Avenue, New Haven, Connecticut. This center publishes the *Quarterly Journal of Studies on Alcohol,* and other scientific literature. It maintains the Abstract Archive of the Alcohol Literature, which contains about 50,000 titles, and annually conducts the Yale Summer School of Alcohol Studies.